S0-BAV-672

Pretty patterns
at the fair —
you can find them
everywhere.

TICKETS

FAIR

③

Green, white, green,
white, green, white —
the pretty lights
are shining bright.

④

Pink, pink, blue,
  pink, pink, blue —
the ferris wheel
  looks pretty, too.

6

Look — a stall
with toys to sell;
there are patterns
here as well.